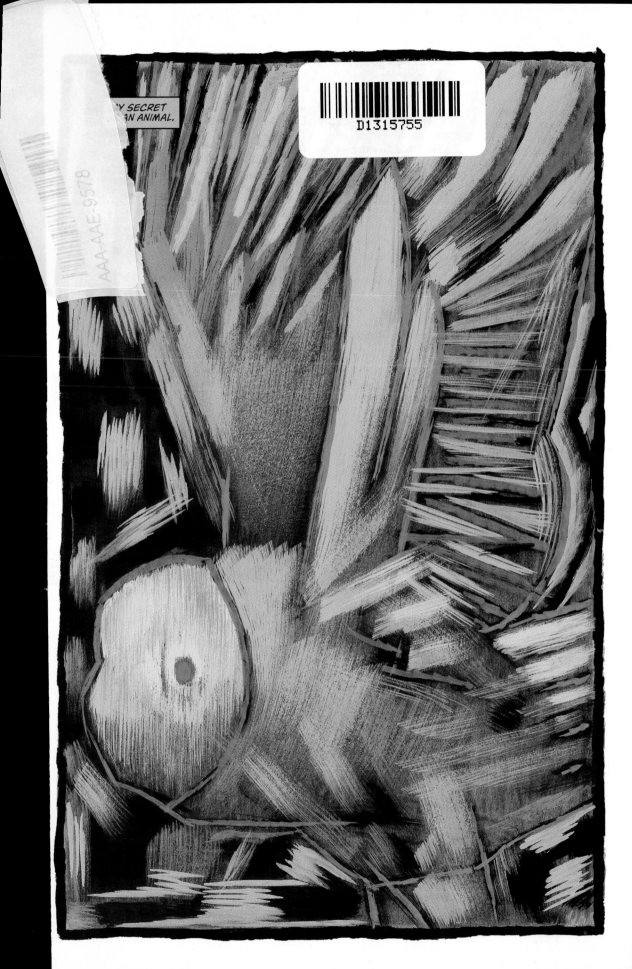

Y SECRET
AN ANIMAL.

AAA-AAE-9578

D1315755

RAIN...?

I TRY TO BE *LIKE* DOROTHY.

I TELL MYSELF, "PAY NO ATTENTION TO THE GIRL BEHIND THE CURTAIN."

BUT EVEN THOUGH *I* DON'T MOVE...

...MY *LEGS* DO...

...BECAUSE THEY'RE NOT REALLY MINE...

...*NOTHING* IS MINE WHEN I'M DEALING WITH THIS HOUSE.

RAIN? ARE YOU OKAY? I SAW YOU OUT IN THE YARD.

I MEAN I WOULDN'T BE AWAKE THIS EARLY, BUT I WAS OUT WITH HOPPER? AND THEN I SNUCK BACK IN?

AND I HEARD THESE SCREAMS, AND I LOOKED OUT AND I SAW--

IF FUCKED-UP GIRLS WITH LIP HERPES HAVE A POSTER CHILD...

...THAT UNLUCKY LITTLE STRUMPET IS VERONICA.

WHAT LITTLE I KNOW OF HER IS SHE HAD EVERY WILLING GUY IN TOWN BEFORE SHE TURNED THIRTEEN...

...AND NOW SHE'S WORKING ON THE UNWILLING...AND IF HOPPER'S INCLUDED, THE *INEPT*.

WORD IS SHE WAS ABANDONED BY HER PARENTS AND ADOPTED OUT, SO SHE'S PROBABLY JUST LOOKING FOR A FATHER FIGURE.

TAKE A NUMBER.

...IT'S BEEN THIS WAY SINCE THE DAWN OF TIME...

...MEN JUMPING UP TO TRY TO PROVE THEMSELVES THE PROTECTORS OF WOMEN...

...WHAT THEY'RE LOOKING FOR IN RETURN IS A SHY, RETIRING WAIF...

...A GIRL WHO BATS HER EYES AND SAYS, "THANK YOU FOR SAVING ME."

NEVER MIND THAT THERE WAS A REVO-LUTION WHERE WE WERE SUPPOSEDLY DECLARED EQUAL...

...NEVER MIND THAT WOMEN FINALLY GOT ON *TOP*...

...TO DENY THE SAVIOR/MARTYR COMPLEX IN A MAN IS TO DENY THE MAN HIMSELF.

LOOK, I KNOW THE BASIS OF OUR RELATIONSHIP IS YOU RUN AND I FOLLOW, BUT--

WHO SAID WE HAVE A RELATION-SHIP?

--BUT *YOU* HAVE TO GIVE SOMETHING *TOO.*

I HAVE NO REASON TO STICK AROUND IF YOU WON'T OPEN UP TO ME, RAIN.

"THERE IS EVIL IN THE WORLD.

"AND AFTER WE ALL SAW IT IN THE WOODS THAT ONE TIME...

"...I MADE EVERYONE GO BACK EXACTLY **ONE** YEAR LATER.

"I WAS JUST GOING TO **SCARE** MY LITTLE MUNCHKIN FRIENDS, BUT WHEN WE GOT THERE...

"...**SATAN** WAS BACK AGAIN...AND HE SAW KIRK.

"WE RAN LIKE HELL AND DIDN'T GO BACK THE NEXT YEAR...

"...THAT WAS THE YEAR KIRK GOT **SNATCHED**.

"AMANDA MADE THE CONNECTION...

"...IF WE DIDN'T GO BACK, BAD SHIT WAS GONNA HAPPEN TO US.

"SO I MADE THE PACT-- WE GO EVERY YEAR NO MATTER WHAT...

"...AND EVERY YEAR THAT WE **HONOR** THE PACT...

"...**SATAN'S** THERE...

"THE RULES ARE SIMPLE...

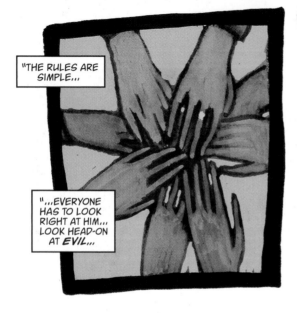

"...EVERYONE HAS TO LOOK RIGHT AT HIM... LOOK HEAD-ON AT **EVIL**...

"...AND GET AWAY BEFORE EVIL LOOKS **BACK**...

"...OR ELSE."

TRUCE...?

COOL.

I NEED A PLACE TO CRASH FOR A WHILE WHERE NO ONE WOULD *EVER* COME LOOKING FOR ME.

JANICE HARPER

YOU LIKE ROSES, DON'T YOU?

IT'S JUST A LITTLE SOMETHING I PICKED UP.

TO WHOM IT MAY CONCERN? WHEN I DIE...WHICH MAY BE *TONIGHT*...

JANICE HARPER

...I DO **NOT** WANT THE TRADITIONAL JUNK...

...NO MATTER **WHOSE** TRADITIONS THEY **ARE**...

...NOT EVEN A LOUISIANA FUNERAL PARADE...

...ALTHOUGH THAT'S GETTING **CLOSER**.

NO, I WANT **FOOD**, AND **ROCK**, AND **PIÑATAS** STUFFED WITH **CASH** AND **CHOCOLATE**...

...I WANT A **PARTY** BIG ENOUGH TO KNOCK THE WORLD OFF ITS AXIS...

...BECAUSE GRAVE-YARDS ARE NO WAY TO REMEMBER PEOPLE.

LOOK, THIS ISN'T GOING TO BE SOME MAJOR SCENE, OKAY?

I JUST...I THINK I'M IN **BIG-TIME** TROUBLE, AND I HAVE TO **TELL** YOU SOMETHING I'VE BEEN HIDING BEFORE I GO...

...I LOVED YOU, MOM...

...AND THAT'S THE ONLY THING LEFT THAT I THINK I'VE NEVER ADMITTED TO ANY-ONE...

WHEN I WAS A KID, I WAS ALWAYS AFRAID OF THIS STREET.

I HAD TO WALK MY BROTHER DOWN IT TO SWIM CLASSES EVERY TUESDAY AND THURSDAY.

BUT IT WASN'T THE WITCH MUSEUM THAT SCARED ME...

...AND IT WASN'T THE WARNINGS FROM MY FATHER ABOUT HOW DANGEROUS A ROAD THIS WAS TO CROSS...

EVERY WEEK IT WAS THE SAME THING...

MAKE SURE YOU LOOK BOTH WAYS.

...HE'D SAY...

I'M COUNTING ON YOU TO LOOK OUT FOR YOUR BROTHER.

I USED TO LAUGH AND TELL MY DAD HE'D BETTER LOOK OUT FOR MY MOM...

...AND HE'D SAY...

I WILL.

...BUT THEN SHE DIED.

THE DAY I RAN AWAY FROM HOME I TOLD MY FATHER THE DEVIL WAS GOING TO GET HIM FOR LYING TO ME.

ARE YOU CRAZY? YOU STEPPED RIGHT IN FRONT OF ME!

HE DIDN'T KNOW WHAT I MEANT THEN...

...I WONDER IF HE DOES NOW.

POLICE

Salem Police
Department

WHAT'D THEY SAY?

I DIDN'T TELL THEM.

BUT, SHE'S DEAD. WE HAVE TO TELL SOMEONE... UM, DON'T WE?

I COULDN'T.

THE THING IS, WE DON'T KNOW THE FULL *TRUTH* ABOUT RAIN.

THE POLICE OR ANYTHING THAT LEADS THE POLICE *TO* HER MIGHT BE BAD FOR HER--ESPECIALLY *TONIGHT.*

COULD YOU GET THAT LIGHT OUT OF--

OH! SORRY!

I'M SO WORRIED ABOUT HER, TRACE.

I THINK SHE REALLY BELIEVES ALL THIS GHOST AND DEVIL JUNK SHE KEEPS TALKING ABOUT.

AND IF YOU *BELIEVE* IN SOMETHING, IT HAS POWER OVER YOU WHETHER IT'S REAL OR NOT.

WE *HAVE* TO HELP HER, I JUST DON'T KNOW HOW...

UM, BEN?

I THINK *I* KNOW...

YOU CAN RUN...
...YOU CAN RUN AND RUN AND RUN...
...YOU CAN TRY...
...BUT YOU CAN NOT HIDE...
...YOU CAN NEVER FORGET...
...YOU CAN'T CHANGE FATE...
THIS... THIS CAN'T BE HERE!
WE'RE NOWHERE NEAR THE SEVEN GABLES!
WHATTA YOU MEAN? WHAT'S--?
...THERE'S NO SUCH THING AS A CLEAN GETAWAY...
OH MY GOD, YOU GUYS! HE'S COMING!
...THE PAST WILL ALWAYS FIND YOU...
...ALWAYS.

AND SOMETIMES SOMETHING YOU'RE NOWHERE NEAR...
...IS STILL NEAR YOU.
INSIDE!
HOPPER! WHERE THE FUCK DID YOU GET THAT?!
IT'S MINE NOW!
THE FUCK IT IS, YOU IDIOT! GIVE ME THAT!
FUCK--
--YOU--
--OOOOFH!
KOOOM!

HE'S RIGHT...IT'S A **NIGHTMARE** TRIBUNAL...

...HEADED BY A LIMBLESS CALIGULA CALLED **CLIUS**...

...RECORDED BY A GRIM GEISHA NAMED **NI AN**,...

...MARSHALED BY THE MESOPOTAMIAN MADMAN **DIGOL**...

...DEFENDED BY THE DEMURELY DECENT **RUBY**,...

...AND PROSECUTED BY THE PLAGUE-ERA PRICK **PFAULTZ.**

It is NO dream!

YOU **CAN'T** BE HERE! I LEFT YOU CREEPS IN SEATTLE!

THIS ISN'T EVEN YOUR **HOUSE!**

We dwell where there are *secrets*...

...children in trash bins, murdered market minders, there are secrets **here.**

I DEMAND A--

YOU DEMAND **NOTHING,** WHELP! YOU ARE WITNESS NO LONGER...

...HE IS.

...HUNNH...?

Welcome home, my dear.

Court is back in session!

SLAMM!

LET GO OF ME YOU CU--

I HOPE YOU'RE NOT ABOUT TO USE THE "C" WORD--

--BECAUSE YOU'LL *REALLY* BE IN TROUBLE IF YOU DO.

LET GO OF ME! WHAT'RE YOU *DOING?*

WHAT I *WAS* DOING WAS FALLING FOR A *TRAP.*

WHAT I *AM* DOING IS PUTTING THE SCREWS TO THE FAT FUCKER *BEHIND* THAT LITTLE FAÇADE...

THE COURT CALLS--

PFAULTZ!

Ah... the main course... *finally.*

I'M NO ONE'S *ENTRÉE,* YOU PLAGUED-OUT PUSS-BAG.

AND I'M NO ONE'S *JUDGE,* EITHER.

YOU THINK YOU CAN TURN ME INTO ONE OF *YOU?*

PLAY OFF MY *PITY* FOR MY FRIENDS BY MAKING ME DRAG THEM IN HERE--

--RIP THE SECRETS OUT OF THEM, PUT THEM ON TRIAL FOR A PAST *I* CREATED?

TRY TO SEAT A *NEW WITNESS* SO I CAN BE TRICKED INTO BECOMING A *JUDGE* AND GIVE YOUR SHITTY SOUL SOME REST?

WELL GET READY FOR AN *ETERNITY* OF DAMNATION, SHITBAG--

--BECAUSE I FIGURED OUT THE WHOLE STORY AND I'M READY TO TELL IT.

ONE TIME... THIS ONE TIME... ONCE UPON A TIME...

"...WE WERE IN THE WOODS.

"AND I TOLD MY FRIENDS THAT I SAW *SATAN* KILLING SOME WOMAN AND THAT THEY BETTER RUN."

"...BUT IT *WASN'T* SATAN...

"...IT WAS FATHER DEMPSEY FROM THE CHURCH DRESSED UP AS A SALEM FOUNDING FATHER FOR THE YEARLY *CARNIVAL*.

"AND HE WASN'T HURTING THE GIRL, HE WAS HELPING HER DELIVER A *BABY*."

GET AWAY FROM HERE AND NEVER TELL ANY-ONE WHAT YOU SAW!

GET AWAY FROM HERE, CHILD!

AND YOU MUSTN'T TELL *ANYONE* WHAT YOU *SAW*! *EVER*...

...FOR HER SAKE.

"WHATEVER THE CASE, WHEN MY FRIENDS RAN AWAY, I STAYED AND WATCHED FROM A DISTANCE.

"THE GIRL DIED IN CHILDBIRTH, AND FATHER DEMPSEY BURIED HER IN THE WOODS.

"WHO KNOWS WHAT SHAME HAD LED TO ALL THIS?

"MAYBE THE KID WAS *HIS*...

"...OR MAYBE HE WAS JUST HELPING A GIRL IN TROUBLE WHEN IT ALL WENT WRONG.

"EITHER WAY, I *FOLLOWED* HIM.

"HE TOOK THE BABY TO THE HOUSE OF SEVEN GABLES AND LEFT IT THERE WITH A NOTE.

"ABOUT THE SAME TIME, A SINGLE MOM WHO WORKED THERE SUDDENLY HAD A NEW DAUGHTER..."

"...A LITTLE BUNDLE OF JOY NAMED **VERONICA.**

"VERONICA WHO GREW UP NAILING EVERYONE IN TOWN LOOKING FOR A DADDY...

"BUT MR. AMERICA, MR. GOLDEN BOY, MR. ALL-AMERICAN DIVER, SUAVE SAM THE PERFECT MAN GOT HER **PREGNANT.**

"HE DIDN'T HAVE THE CASH FOR AN ABORTION SO HE KILLED A 7-11 GUY AND ROBBED HIM...

"...BUT THEN USED THE MONEY TO BUY A HOT LITTLE RED **MUSTANG** HE COULDN'T PASS UP.

"HE LET VERONICA HAVE HER BABY, KEPT IT HIDDEN, THEN TRIED TO GET RID OF IT JUST LIKE SHE'D BEEN GOTTEN RID OF YEARS EARLIER...

"...BECAUSE A SECRET KEPT IS A SECRET THAT GAINS POWER AND KEEPS ON GETTING STRONGER.

"...EVERYONE **INCLUDING** SAMIR KASIM.

"AND A SECRET NOT CONFRONTED IS A SECRET THAT GROWS LIKE A TUMOR, SENDING OUT SPORES TO START ALL OVER AGAIN.

"NOT HAVING LEARNED THE LESSON HIS DICK **TRIED** TO TEACH HIM THE FIRST TIME, SAM STARTED A SECRET ROMANCE. TWO TO BE EXACT.

"...AND ONE WITH MARLITA--WHO HE LOVED SO MUCH HE DIDN'T EVEN TELL HER THAT HE KNEW HER LONG LOST BROTHER WAS STILL LONG LOST.

"ONE WITH AMANDA...

"HELL, HE'D PROBABLY HAVE GONE AFTER **CARLOS** IF THERE'D BEEN MORE HOURS IN THE DAY."

SO I GIVE YOU SAM. ALL OF THE SECRETS ARE HIS.

NO DOUBT YOU WERE HOPING I'D MAKE HIM *CONFESS,* AND HAVING DELIVERED EVERY LAST ONE OF MY LITTLE CIRCLE TO YOU I'D DAMN MYSELF TO BECOMING JURIS: THE NEXT GENERATION.

BUT WHILE SAM'S *DEFINITELY* GOING TO PAY FOR HIS SECRETS...

...HE'LL PAY IN *MY* WORLD, NOT *YOURS.*

YOUR OLD FRIEND *MAAT* WARNED ME THAT IF I FAILED IN TRIAL I'D BE CONDEMNED--

--BUT SHE DIDN'T MEAN IF I WAS FOUND *GUILTY.* SHE MEANT IF I COULDN'T LIVE UP TO BEING THE *WITNESS* TO SECRETS.

WELL GUESS WHAT? I *CAN,* AND I *DID.*

I BUST SECRETS LIKE NOBODY'S BUSINESS-- SAM'S *AND* MINE...

...SECRETS NO LONGER, BECAUSE WE'RE HERE IN EACH OTHER'S HUMAN PRESENCE.

CASE CLOSED.

KRA-KOOM!

...FOR ALL THE BOOKWORMS OUT THERE...

IT'S OVER. IT'S FINALLY--

...OR MORE IMPORTANT, FOR ALL THE *PSEUDO-*INTELLECTUALS WHO ACTUALLY NEVER READ *ANYTHING--*

--THERE'S THIS STORY, "THE LADY OR THE TIGER"...

THUMP
THUMP
THUMP
THUMP

...IN IT, THIS GUY HAS TO CHOOSE BETWEEN TWO DOORS...

...BEHIND ONE IS A *LADY*-- BEAUTIFUL, FUCKABLE, A-LIST-SUPER-MODEL-HAREM-GIRL-WET-DREAM FANTASY MATERIAL...

...BEHIND THE *OTHER* IS A *BENGAL*--HUNGRY, SINEWY, AND READY FOR A LITTLE HOMOSAPIEN SOUFFLE...

...THE STORY BUILDS AND BUILDS AND BUILDS WITH THE GUY MAKING HIS WAY TO THE DOORS AND THEN TRYING TO DECIDE WHICH ONE TO PICK.

IT'S HUGE DRAMA--HOT ANIMAL *SEX?* OR HOT ANIMAL *LUNCH?*

BUT THEN THE STORY ENDS BEFORE HE MAKES THE CHOICE. THE READER NEVER KNOWS WHICH DOOR HE OPENED.

I ALWAYS *HATED* THAT STORY...

...BECAUSE I *WANT* TO KNOW HOW THINGS *END.*

BESIDES, I'VE GOT NOTHING TO FEAR FROM SATAN ANYMORE...

...THIS LADY *IS* A TIGER.

CLACK

...DAD...? HOW DID YOU...?

WE WERE FOLLOWING YOU THROUGH THE WOODS, BUT YOU LOST US FOR A WHILE WHEN YOU RAN AHEAD. WE--

WE HOPE YOU AREN'T *MAD*, RAIN, BUT WE, UM... WELL--

WE READ IN YOUR JOURNAL THAT YOU ALWAYS WANTED TO TELL YOUR DAD ABOUT FATHER DEMPSEY AND THE FOREST, AND UH...

...WE THOUGHT MAYBE YOU DIDN'T KNOW *HOW*, SO WHEN YOUR AUNT DIED--

OH YEAH, LOTTIE, UM, CROAKED. BAD.

--WE HAD TO TELL *SOMEONE*, AND... WELL ANYWAY, WE HOPE YOU AREN'T *MAD* AT US.

I'M SORRY, HONEY. I KNOW I WASN'T THERE TO LISTEN WHEN YOU WERE HURTING. BUT YOU DIDN'T HAVE TO *LEAVE.*

I LOVE YOU. DON'T FORGET THAT.

...I COULD NEVER FORGET...

End

DC Comics

JENETTE KAHN President & Editor-in-Chief

PAUL LEVITZ Executive Vice President & Publisher

KAREN BERGER Executive Editor

SHELLY BOND Editor

WILL DENNIS Associate Editor

MARK CHIARELLO Editorial Art Director

MARIA CABARDO Art Director

RICHARD BRUNING VP-Creative Director

PATRICK CALDON Senior VP-Finance & Operations

DOROTHY CROUCH VP-Licensed Publishing

TERRI CUNNINGHAM VP-Managing Editor

JOEL EHRLICH Senior VP-Advertising & Promotions

ALISON GILL Executive Director-Manufacturing

LILLIAN LASERSON VP & General Counsel

JIM LEE Editorial Director-WildStorm

JOHN NEE VP & General Manager-WildStorm

CHERYL RUBIN VP-Licensing & Merchandising

They thought the past was dead and buried. But in truth, the hidden secrets of "the Salem Seven" have pushed themselves up out of their shallow, muddy graves. Now they stalk the nighttime forest like Bengal tigers hungry for prey.

house of secrets
FACADE

RAIN HARPER HAS ONCE MORE SET IN MOTION THE WHEELS OF A HORRIFYING ANNUAL RITUAL. BUT THIS TIME SOMETHING IS DIFFERENT. A CONSTRICTING WEB OF INTERTWINED SECRETS IS THREATENING TO CHOKE THE VERY LIFE FROM RAIN, HER CHILD-HOOD FRIENDS, AND HER NEWFOUND ALLIES ALIKE.

AT THE CENTER OF IT ALL IS RAIN HERSELF. TRYING TO ESCAPE HER WEST COAST HAUNTERS—THE VINDICTIVE, ETHEREAL EMBODIMENT OF JUDGMENT KNOWN AS THE JURIS—RAIN HAS FLED TO SALEM, MASSACHUSETTS ONLY TO FIND THAT WHERE SHE GOES—THE SPIRITS FOLLOW. LOST IN THE WOODS, RAIN MUST CHOOSE—THE SACRIFICE OF HER CLOSEST FRIENDS OR ETERNAL DAMNATION IN THE FORM OF HER OWN SEAT ON THE JURIS. AND SHE'D BETTER DECIDE QUICKLY BECAUSE—

Satan is hot on her heels.

THE DEVIL BEHIND ONE DOOR, CERTAIN DAMNATION BEHIND THE OTHER. WHICH HELL WILL RAIN HARPER CHOOSE?

The answer to that question is at the core of HOUSE OF SECRETS: FACADE, a 2-issue miniseries written by STEVEN T. SEAGLE (THE CRUSADES, SANDMAN MYSTERY THEATRE) and exquisitely painted by TEDDY KRISTIANSEN (THE SANDMAN, SANDMAN MIDNIGHT THEATRE).

TT-439-263

DIRECT SALES

00211